... was a primary teacher and headteacher. He
... in teacher training and was English Inspector in
Gloucestershire. He advises the National Literacy
Strategy, especially on teaching poetry, writing and
grammar. He writes training materials and has run
Inservice across the country. The author of over a
hundred books, a poet and storyteller, he spends much of
his time irritating editors by not answering the phone
because he is making up poems or daydreaming.

Poems for Year 4

chosen by
Pie Corbett

MACMILLAN CHILDREN'S BOOKS

First published 2002
by Macmillan Children's Books
a division of Macmillan Publishers Limited
20 New Wharf Road, London N1 9RR
Basingstoke and Oxford
www.panmacmillan.com

Associated companies throughout the world

ISBN 0 330 48289 0

1 3 5 7 9 8 6 4 2

A CIP catalogue record for this book is available from the British Library.
Printed by Mackays of Chatham plc, Chatham, Kent.

Contents

Introduction

An anthology is like a gathering of old friends. I'd like you to meet some of mine. Many of these poems I have known for a long time. They are so strong that the passing of time seems to have enriched their meaning. But there are also some new additions – fresh sparks that caught my eye like sudden gleams of sunlight. Sharply cut diamonds that reflect some facet of who we are.

I suppose I am lucky – my group of poetry friends is large. So, how was I to choose the sixty or so poems for this book? Well, in a way it was easy enough. At first hundreds of old chums jostled for attention. But I wanted poems that I had shared with children on many occasions. Poems that I knew would appeal, would interest and fascinate. Poems that would resonate in the mind long after their reading. So they had to be strong poems.

I wanted to bring together poems that were related – so that they would sometimes speak to each other in their own language, echoing back and forth across the pages. I wanted to have poems that I knew would not always be too easily grasped. Poems that might need thinking about. Not everything in life is easy to understand and sometimes the most mysterious are the most amazing – I could never fathom how a magnet works, but they have always fascinated me. Why don't rainbows wobble in the wind? Just because things are difficult to understand does not mean they cannot intrigue, or be beautiful. Poems are not like simple sums – these old friends cannot always be tied down easily, but meet them, greet them and enjoy them.

And I wanted poems that could act as a kick-start to writing. Many of these poems are old standbys – faithful retainers, who have helped thousands of children find poetry within themselves, a self-confidence to put a word in, their word. Many of these poems have been the catalyst to children's own writing – and I have been lucky enough to witness some remarkable poems being written, in moments when something of our common genius poked its nose round the corner to surprise us all. So, I needed poems that I knew could strengthen imagination, release invention and ignite writing. If you like, this collection is a toolbox for creative teachers, readers and writers.

Finally, I imagined myself with a class of Year 4 children and thought about what poetry equipment we might need to take us through the journey of a year together. Poems that we could lean upon, poems that would surprise us, poems of many shades and moods. Poems that did not patronize. Poems that might light up a lifetime.

I wanted the poems to reflect the National Literacy Strategy. I thought it would be handy to have a good collection, easily accessible. So, there are poems built around themes (can you spot them?), some classic and many modern, poems from a variety of cultures as well as poems in all sorts of different forms. All this is included – but, to be honest, while this helped to sharpen the choice, it never hindered. And besides, I wanted poems so strong that they would speak to others – those interested in writing in other year groups and beyond. Not just poems written for a nine year old, but poems that had demanded to be written.

So, step inside – meet this gathering of old friends and relations. Give them some time and you will get to know them well – and, maybe, make friends for life. You may even be tempted to create a few – take a step out of the darkness of yourself. Step into sunlight. It feels good to make new friends, to create something new.

Pie Corbett
April 2002

Hippopotamus

Baked mud, small threads of the river
drawn through wet silt; the African sun
batters the senses, while mosquitoes
drone in the thrumming heat.

Down in the weed-choked wallows
bathes the Lord of the old water:
heavy, hard-skinned, hard-tusked,
his head is a slick iron hammer.

Under the sun's eye, the great beast
rolls in the soft mire, slowly
dreaming of wide savannahs
where cool streams run green
under palms wet with birdsong;
and there are no guns, no hunters.

Tony Charles

Hippo Writes a Love Poem to His Wife

Oh my beautiful fat wife
Larger to me than life
Smile broader than the river Nile
My winsome waddlesome
You do me proud in the shallow of morning
You do me proud in the deep of night
Oh, my bodysome mud-basking companion.

Hippo Writes a Love Poem to Her Husband

Oh my lubby-dubby hubby-hippo
With your widely-winning lippo
My Sumo-thrasher of water
Dearer to me than any two-legger
How can I live without
Your ponderful potamus pout?

John Agard

Gorilla . . .

has a mouth
like a watermelon inside.

Teeth like seeds
when he yawns.
Eyes

like a coal black
old pit stack
smouldering there.

Did he stare?
Did he glare?

He makes me afraid.

Strange worlds in his look.
And his coat

dark as night
with bright

equatorial

stars.

Ann Bonner

We Must Be Polite

(Lessons for children on how to behave under peculiar circumstances)

1

If we meet a gorilla
what shall we do?

Two things we may do
if we so wish to do.

Speak to the gorilla
very, very respectfully,
'How do you do, sir?'

Or, speak to him with less
distinction of manner,
'Hey, why don't you go back
where you came from?'

2

If an elephant knocks on your door
and asks for something to eat,
there are two things to say:

Tell him there are nothing but cold
victuals in the house and he will do
better next door.

Or say: We have nothing but six bushels
of potatoes – will that be enough for
your breakfast, sir?

Carl Sandburg

Blake's Tyger – Revisited

*On hearing that tigers in captivity can gradually lose their colour,
losing their camouflaging stripes and fading gradually to white.*

Tiger! Tiger! Turning white
In a cage just twice your height
Six paces left, six paces right,
A long slow day, a longer night.

Tiger! Tiger! Dreaming still
Of the scent? The chase? The kill?
And now? No need. No place. No scope.
No space. No point. No hope.

Tiger! Tiger! Paces. Paces.
Once he flashed through open spaces.
His world once echoed to his roars.
Now he's quiet. He stares. He snores.

An inch of sky glimpsed through the bars.
A puddle. Concrete. Smells of cars.
He sniffs the air. He slumps. He sighs.
And stares and stares through jaundiced eyes.

Michaela Morgan

The Magnificent Bull

My bull is white like the silver fish in the river
white like the shimmering crane bird on the river
  bank
white like fresh milk!
His roar is like the thunder to the Turkish cannon on
  the steep shore.
My bull is dark like the raincloud in the storm.
He is like summer and winter.
Half of him is dark like the storm cloud,
half of him is light like sunshine.
His back shines like the morning star.
His brow is red like the beak of the Hornbill.
His forehead is like a flag, calling the people from a
  distance,
He resembles the rainbow.

I will water him at the river,
With my spear I shall drive my enemies.
Let them water their herds at the well;
the river belongs to me and my bull.
Drink, my bull, from the river; I am here
to guard you with my spear.

Dinka tribe (Sudan)

The Locust

What is a locust?
Its head, a grain of corn; its neck, the hinge of a knife;
Its horns, a bit of thread; its chest is smooth and
   burnished;
Its body is like a knife-handle;
Its hock, a saw; its spittle, ink;
Its underwings, clothing for the dead.
On the ground – it is laying eggs;
In flight – it is like the clouds.
Approaching the ground, it is rain glittering in the sun;
Lighting on a plant, it becomes a pair of scissors;
Walking, it becomes a razor;
Desolation walks with it.

Trad. (Madagascar)

Translated by A. Marre and Willard R. Trask

A Stick Insect

A stick insect
is not a thick insect,
a macho-built-like-a-brick insect,
a brawl-and-break-it-up-quick insect,
not a sleek-and-slippery-slick insect
or a hold-out-your-hand-for-a-lick insect.

No way could you say it's a cuddly pet
or a butterfly that hasn't happened yet.

And it won't come running when you call
or chase about after a ball.
And you can't take it out for a walk
or try to teach it how to talk.

It's a hey-come-and-look-at-this-quick insect,
a how-can-you-tell-if-it's-sick insect,
a don't-mistake-me-for-a-stick insect . . .

Brian Moses

May Bugs

We could hear them on summer nights
Clatter against the wire fences of the tennis courts.
Kevin, who did not mind handling those
Huge grey-brown bugs, would
Smuggle them in matchboxes
Into the chaos of our French lessons
And release them,
Secretly,
At intervals,
Great lumbering jumbo bugs
Would blunder at head height
Across the classroom of
Ducking children, flying books
And Mr Johnson
Whose anger was spectacular.

Chris Eddershaw

Porch Light

At night
the porch light
catches moths
and holds them,
trapped
and
flapping,
in a tight
yellow fist.
Only when I
turn the switch
will it loosen
its hot
grip.

Deborah Chandra

Birdfoot's Grampa

The old man
must have stopped our car
two dozen times to climb out
and gather into his hands
the small toads blinded
by our light and leaping,
live drops of rain.

The rain was falling,
a mist about his white hair
and I kept saying
you can't save them all,
accept it, get back in
we've got places to go.

But, leathery hands full
of wet brown life,
knee deep in the summer
roadside grass,
he just smiled and said
they have places to go, too.

Joseph Bruchac

Hopping Frog

Hopping frog, hop here and be seen,
I'll not pelt you with stick or stone:
Your cap is laced and your coat is green;
Goodbye, we'll let each other alone.

Christina Rossetti

My Cat Syllable

Mine. Who lies all afternoon
on the neighbour's wall drinking
sunlight, a black rag dumped out
of bottomless space on the
back garden lawn, sprawled flat on
flower beds. Who does he really
belong to?

       Darkness. Two green
lamps flare in darkness. He has
drunk the sun, now the moon is
at risk. Turning his back he
dons invisibility
like the lightest tightest glove.

Brian Morse

Cat in the Window

Cat in the window,
  what do you see?

Cloud, wind, leaves,
  a bird in a tree.

The daffodils shivering
  in the February breeze,

A puddle in the road
  beginning to freeze.

Snow on the wind,
  dusk in a cloud,

Leaves in a frenzy,
  the bird's head cowed.

Winter – though the sun shines
  Blizzard, and the north wind's whine.

Brian Morse

Rat Race

Rat Race?
Don't make us laugh.
It's you humans
who're always in a haste.

Ever seen a rat
in a bowler hat
rushing to catch a train?

Ever seen a rat
with a briefcase
hurrying through the rain?

And isn't it a fact
that all that hurry-hurry
gives you humans heart attacks?

No, my friend,
we rats relax.

Pass the cheese,
please.

John Agard

Snout Doing

Said Hedgehog to Badger,
'Oh, let's marry, do –
we'll shickle and pruffle and sup hogger stew,
we'll insect each other with lice evermore,
have badgehogs in batches
and hedgers galore.
We'll live till we snuffit
twogether as one.'

Said Badger to Hedgehog,
'Oh, fleas run along.
I do get your point but I'm sett in my ways
and thoroughly sick of rollmantic displays
so don't take a fence, Hedge,
but this is my plot –
just go hog a headlight
and badger me not.'

Gina Douthwaite

Message for the Mosquito Who Shares My Bedroom

I'm fed up
with the way
you keep me awake.
You wait
till I've just turned the light off
and settled down
for a good night's zizzzzzz
before starting up
your irritating whine.
Announcing,
'Mister Mosquito
is out for a bite.'
At any second
I expect to feel you
puncture my skin
and suck my blood.
Tiny vampire,
I am not your personal
ketchup bottle.
If I find you've settled nearby,
I'll swat you flat.
Be warned –
go pester
some other sauce
of blood.

Pie Corbett

Self-Advert for Mole Programme Tonight

My name is Mole.
I inhabit a hole
and pooter about in the dark.

I make my way
through earth and clay
under the lamb and the lark.

Tunnelling my run
far from the sun
I dig like a JCB.

I climb from my lair
and sniff the air –
tonight on BBC.

Robert Hull

Rabbit and Dragon

Not a fair comparison, really:
dragons don't live in hutches.
They do have shining scales,
great eyelids, burning breath.
They don't eat mash and meal
at thirty pence a pound
from the pet shop.

They sleep
long ages on their beds of gold.
People make songs about them

But rabbits don't eat children.
And nobody hunts them with bright spears.

I'd rather be a dragon
but rabbit's easier.

Tony Charles

The Day the Zoo Escaped

The day the zoo escaped . . .

the zebras zipped out quickly,
the snakes slid out slickly,

the lions marched out proudly,
the hyenas laughed out loudly,

the mice skipped out lightly,
the parrots flew out brightly,

but the hippopotamus,
stubbornly,

just stayed where it was.

Michaela Morgan and Sue Palmer

An Animal Alphabet

Alligator, beetle, porcupine, whale,
Bobolink, panther, dragonfly, snail,
Crocodile, monkey, buffalo, hare,
Dromedary, leopard, mud-turtle, bear,
Elephant, badger, pelican, ox,
Flying fish, reindeer, anaconda, fox,
Guinea pig, dolphin, antelope, goose,
Hummingbird, weasel, pickerel, moose,
Ibex, rhinoceros, owl, kangaroo,
Jackal, opossum, toad, cockatoo,
Kingfisher, peacock, anteater, bat,
Lizard, ichneumon, honeybee, rat,
Mockingbird, camel, grasshopper, mouse,
Nightingale, spider, cuttlefish, grouse,
Ocelot, pheasant, wolverine, auk,
Periwinkle, ermine, katydid, hawk,
Quail, hippopotamus, armadillo, moth,
Rattlesnake, lion, woodpecker, sloth,
Salamander, goldfinch, angleworm, dog,
Tiger, flamingo, scorpion, frog,
Unicorn, ostrich, nautilus, mole,
Viper, gorilla, basilisk, sole,
Whippoorwill, beaver, centipede, fawn,
Xantho, canary, polliwog, swan,
Yellowhammer, eagle, hyena, lark,
Zebra, chameleon, butterfly, shark.

Anon.

Miss! Sue is Kissing

Miss! Sue is kissing
the tadpoles again.
She is, Miss. I did,
I asked her. She said
something about catching
him young. Getting one
her own age. I don't know,
Miss. She keeps whispering
'Prince, Prince,' Isn't that
a dog's name, Miss?

Michael Harrison

... *And After a Hundred Years Had Passed, Sleeping Beauty Awoke (At Last!) from Her Slumber*

The drawbridge is creaking
The castle is leaking.
The royal crown is rusting.
The throne room needs dusting.
Cobwebs hang from my crystal chandeliers.
How can you ask a princess
To deal with this terrible mess?
Wake me again in another hundred years.

Judith Viorst

. . . And Beauty and the Beast, Once the Spell Had Been Broken, Lived Happily (Sort of Happily) Ever After

It was fun to be the best-looking one in the palace.
It was fun to get all the compliments and applause.
Yes, I was a pearl among girls
With my milky-white skin and bright curls,
While he was the hairy beast with the snout and claws.

It was fun to be the best-looking one in the palace.
It was fun – till the spell was broken and he was released
To become a prince so divine
that his gorgeousness far outshone mine.
Now everyone thinks he's the beauty and I'm the beast.

Judith Viorst

... And While Poor Hansel Was Locked in the Witch's Cage, Awaiting His Doom, Clever Gretel Came to Her Brother's Rescue

The witch had dinner reservations.
(My brother was the dinner.)
I was the clever person who made her cancel.
I gave her a shove in
The burning oven.
My brother owes me his life.
So why don't they call this story
'Gretel and Hansel'?

Judith Viorst

Mister Butcher-Bird

Please,
Mr Butcher-bird,
What have you got
Today?
Can I have some roast beef?
What is that
You say?
Only got a caterpillar!
Not a mutton chop?
No,
Mr Butcher-bird,
I'll have to change
My shop!

The Perfesser and
Alter Ego

What's Your Name?

What's your name?
Johnny Maclean.
Where do you live?
Down the lane.
What's your shop?
Lollypop.
What's your number?
Cucumber.

What's your name?
Mary Jane.
Where do you live?
Cabbage Lane.
What's your number?
Rain and thunder.
What address?
Watercress.

Anon.

A House of Bricks

Oh, it's that old game,
the making-up-the-collective-noun
game. I'm good at that.

They come to me as easy as fish
come to the shop in a van
from Grimsby. A field

of crop circles. A van of fish.
That's the kind of thing.
Collective nouns are easy.

A hair net of hair.
A sunset of clouds.
A case of matching luggage.

It's easy this. Goodnight.
Keep in touch. A keep in touch
of friends. A calendar of months.

A fiery hell. Maybe not quite,
that one. Maybe not.
Language is so easy, so

easy. Goodnight all.
Keep in touch.

Ian McMillan

DIY UFO Poem

Umbrella Fights Officer?
Unapproachable Fish Offside?
Uncanny Frog Objects?

Unfold Furled Omelette?
Unattached Fabulous Oarsman?
Underpants Fumigate Oldham?

Try your own DIY UFO Poem!

upside down, unlikely,
unload, underground,
united, uncle,
uncanny, uncertain,
ultimate, unbolt,
Hugh, unbeaten,
unbutton, unaware,
unassuming,
unapproachable,
under, unable,
umbrella, under,
unattached,
ugly, ultimate,
unwind, unscramble,
unmentionable,
unconscious,
uncork, unlikely,
underground,
underpants,
undeveloped,
understand,
unfold,
unique,
ungovernable,
u-turn

fade, fish,
fashionable, fabric
fabulous, face, facts,
fiddle, fail, fair/fare,
fat, fall, false, fame,
feel, faint, ferocious,
fit, fill, film, fine,
find, fix, first, flatten,
flood, fly, fume,
follow, foggy, force,
forget, forge, forfeit,
foul, fighting, free,
fritter, frog, fry, fuse,
funnel, futuristic,
fuzzy, fun, fumigate,
frolic, front, friendly,
frequently, frizzle
first, flibberty-gibbet,
formidable, form,
forlorn, foreign, first,
French,
foreboding, foolish,
fraudulent,
Filofax,
flummoxed

obligation, oak,
oath, oarsman,
oar, oatmeal,
obedient, obelisk,
obesity, oboe,
observation,
obnoxious,
obscure,
observant, ocean,
obsession,
obsolete, obstacle,
obstinacy,
obvious, occasion,
occupation,
occupant, October,
octuplets, oddball,
odd, offence,
official, offside,
offshore, offspring,
okay, Oldham,
Olympic, omelette,
one-stop, ozone,
ooze, opposite,
onomatopoeia,
outrageous

UNIDENTIFIED   FLYING   OBJECT

Judith Nicholls

Where?

where do you hide a leaf?
in, if possib*le, a f*orest.

where do you hide a wind?
among a stra*w in d*ust.

where do you hide a horse?
within a clo*th or se*a.

where do you hide the sun?
behind cloud*s, un*der
   horizons.

where do you hide water?
belo*w a ter*rible flood.

where do you hide a storm?
inside a gho*st or m*agician.

where do you hide a word?

Dave Calder

Sought it Out!

The rider pulled on the rain
(and got soaking wet for his trouble).

He rowed to the key.
(it opened but he could not land).

He tried to sew a pattern
(but nothing grew in the field).

He combed his hare
(but it struggled to escape).

He followed its cent
(and had enough to pay for pair).

He cooked fresh bread with flower
(and ate a primrose loaf).

He sheltered beneath an old yew
(but its bleating woke him).

He watched the night put on his spurs
(they gleamed like stars).

He climbed the Queen's stare to bed
(and slept in her eyes).

He was pleased to reach the end of the tail
(to his surprise it wagged happily).

Pie Corbett

How Did He Escape?

There was a man
in prison who was
famous for escaping –
left all his captors gaping.

So they built him a room
like a mummy's tomb
in their finest gaol
and left him there to rot –
not a jot of a chance
to escape –
no windows,
and the doors held fast
with the largest lock
they had in stock!

All he had inside the room
was a wooden table –
and yet,
according to the fable,
ten minutes later
he was free –

So, tell me, tell me,
Alligator –
how was it done?

Pie Corbett

answer on page 118

The Tale of the Cleverest Son

Once, not twice,
but once, there lived
an elderly man
with sons – one, two, three.
Knowing,
he would soon be dead,
he called them to his bed
and said,

'I have decided
that when I die
the cleverest of three
should receive all that I have
in this world . . .'
And on to the table he hurled
three coins.
'Take one each
and go into town.
Buy what you like.
The one
who can fill
this room with the most
will inherit all that I own.'

With a groan,
the oldest filled
a wagon with bales of straw.
The second son killed
a farmyard of turkeys,
filled sack after sack
with feathers.
But the third,
slipped into a shop
and bought two
small packets
that he tucked out of sight.

That night
the father called his sons
to show how wisely
they had spent.

The oldest lad
emptied the wagon
but the straw only
covered the floor.
The second son
dragged up the sacks
and feathers flew
in all directions
but they too settled back,
barely covering the carpet.

Then the youngest son
took out two small packets
and a moment later
he had filled the room . . .

Now my question to you
is simply this –
what was it
that so easily flooded
the room . . . ?

Answer

No scandal –
he bought a candle –
No catch –
he bought a match.
And let light
dispel gloom
to fill the room.

Pie Corbett

Jargon

Jerusalem, Joppa, Jericho –
These are the cities of long ago.

Jasper, jacinth, jet and jade
of such are jewels for ladies made.

Juniper's green and jasmine's white,
Sweet jonquil is spring's delight.

Joseph, Jeremy, Jennifer, James,
Julian, Juliet – just names.

January, July and June –
Birthday late or birthday soon

Jacket, jersey, jerkin, jeans –
What's the wear for sweet sixteens?

Jaguar, jackal, jumbo, jay –
Came to dinner but couldn't stay.

Jellies, junkets, jumbals, jam –
Mix them up for a sweet-toothed Sam.

To jig, to jaunt, to jostle, to jest –
These are the things that Jack loves best.

Jazz, jamboree, jubilee, joke –
The jolliest words you ever spoke.

From A to Z and Z to A
The joyfullest letter of all is J.

James Reeves

Taking the Plunge

One day a boy said to a girl in a swimming pool
'I'm going to dive in, are you?' She replied
'No thanks. I bet you can't anyway.' So the boy
got on the diving board and dived and said
'See.' The girl replied 'Flipping 'eck!'

(Simon Wilkinson)

Flipping 'eck, cor blimey, strewth,
You're my hero, that's the honest truth.

Lumme, crikey, lordy lord,
It's a long way down from that diving board.

Itchy beard and stone the crows,
Don't you get chlorine up your nose?

Luv a duck and strike me pink,
You're slicker than the soap in the kitchen sink.

Knock me down with a sparrow's feather,
How about us going out together?

Groovy, t'riffic, brill and smashing,
Me 'n' you, we could start things splashing.

Wotcha cocky, ta-ra, see ya,
Meet me for a Coke in the cafeteria.

Hallelujah and amen,
If you like this poem you can read it again.

John Mole

Playing a Dazzler

You bash drums playing a dazzler;
I worry a trumpet swaying with it.

You dance, you make a girl's skirt swirl;
I dance, I dance by myself.

You bowl, I lash air and my wicket;
I bowl, you wallop boundary balls.

Your goal-kick beat me between my knees;
my goal-kick flies into a pram-and-baby.

You eat off your whole-pound chocolate cake;
I swell up halfway to get my mate's help.

My bike hurls me into the hedge;
your bike swerves half-circle from trouble.

I jump the wall and get dumped;
you leap over the wall and laugh, satisfied.

I touch the country bridge and walk;
you talk and talk.

You write poems with line-end rhymes;
I write poems with rhymes nowhere or anywhere.

Your computer game screens monsters and gunners;
my game brings on swimmers and courting red-birds.

James Berry

Sometimes

Sometimes the mischief of your grin
Is the label on a box with nothing in.

Sometimes the furrow of your frown
Is misery smiling upside-down.

Sometimes the hammer of your laugh
Is enough to split my world in half.

Sometimes you simply wait to see
Which of your tricks work best on me.

John Mole

The Dare

1

Steep banks
and oozing mud
are all I see below;
no friends, just voices jeering: 'Yes –
or no?'

2

Go on,
I dare you, jump!
Mud lapped with water swims
before my eyes; behind, in dreams,
I drown.

Judith Nicholls

Waiting

In the dentist's waiting room I'm
nervid
wunxious
fothered
anxit
weeful
wobbered
tummled
glumpit
frettled
horrish
gumshot
dismy
squawbid
grimlip
dregless –
IT'S ME!

Sue Cowling

Funny How She Forgets

Funny how she forgets
Her PE kit on Mondays –
Not on Fridays when it's gym,
Not on Wednesdays when they swim
Monday is hockey with Mrs Betts –
Funny how she forgets.

Sue Cowling

from Snap. Shots.

the first time i saw
my mum take her teeth out
i thought it was wonderful
must have been five
and i tried and i tried
but i couldn't get my teeth
to slippin' and slide out
no way could i capture
the click an' no doubt
as she took her teeth out
the matter o' fact
as she clacked 'er teeth back.

Labi Siffre

Trying it On

I used to sneak into my sister's room
when she was out.
I pinched her lipstick, made my mirrored mouth
a cherry pout.

One time I found this bronzing tube and creamed
my spotty face
By break I was a tan-streaked member of
the Asian race.

The Head was mad and wrote a letter home –
my mam was tamping.
She banned me from the treasure drawers and
left me stamping.

She said 'No more of that, young brazen miss!'
(like brass, it means)
Instead I tried on heaps of sister-clothes,
her tops and jeans.

When I am sixteen I will be a model,
look so ultra-cool.
It's not fair I can't have stuff of my own
to make boys drool.

I peeked in when our Anne was kissing Dai,
just for some tips.
She caught me, threw a shoe and said,
'You're pushing your luck, you are!'

Jean Gill

Playground Song

I'm the one in calipers
Who makes the people stare –
I used to lie awake at night
And think it wasn't fair,
But since I've found a proper friend
I really couldn't care . . .

She told her mum
                  that I'm the one
With lovely curly hair.

Clare Bevan

Such Times

I walk across the playground. And all of a sudden
a six-year-old boy rushes to me
with wild strawberry cheeks.
In his hand he clutches a pop gun.
'Bang! Bang!' – he shoots at me.
Then he sticks the weapon in his pocket.
'Gotcha!' – he says and runs off.

I notify the family. Friends.
I phone the police and report my death.
They spread their helpless hands.
'Such times' – they say.

Ewa Lipska (Poland)

And My Heart Soars

The beauty of the trees,
the softness of the air,
the fragrance of the grass,
    speaks to me.

The summit of the
  mountain,
the thunder of the sky,
the rhythm of the sea,
    speaks to me.

The faintness of the stars,
the freshness of the morning,
the dew drop on the flower,
    speaks to me.

The strength of the fire,
the taste of salmon,
the trail of the sun,
and the life that never goes
  away,
    they speak to me.

And my heart soars.

Chief Dan George

In My Country

In my country they jail you
For what they think you think.
My uncle once said to me:
They'll implant a microchip
In our minds
To flash our thoughts and dreams
On to a screen at John Vorster Square.
I was scared:
By day I guard my tongue
By night my dreams.

Pitika Ntuli
(South Africa)

Young Africa's Lament

I am half starved;
I asked for bread they gave me stone.
I am thirsty;
I asked for water they gave me slush.
They tell the horse to wait awhile
Because green grasses would soon grow
And dry Sahara would yield great streams.

Dennis Chukude Osadebay
(Nigeria)

from Dry Your Tears, Africa!

Dry your tears, Africa!
Your children come back to you
their hands full of presents
and their hearts full of love.
They return to clothe you
in their dreams and their hopes.

Bernard Dadié
(Côte d'Ivoire)

Mama Dot

Born on a Sunday
in the kingdom of Ashante

Sold on a Monday
into slavery

Ran away on Tuesday
'cause she born free

Lost a foot on Wednesday
when they catch she

Worked all Thursday
till her hair grey

Dropped on a Friday
when they burned she

Freed on a Saturday
in a new century

Fred D'Aguiar

Swing Low

Swing low, sweet chariot,
Coming for to carry me home!
Swing low, sweet chariot,
Coming for to carry me home!

I looked over Jordan and what did I see?
Coming for to carry me home!
A band of angels coming after me,
Coming for to carry me home!

If you get there before I do,
Coming for to carry me home!
Tell all my friends I'm coming too,
Coming for to carry me home!

Swing low, sweet chariot,
Coming for to carry me home!
Swing low, sweet chariot,
Coming for to carry me home!

Trad.
(USA)

Cradle Song

Did you look near the loch?
And what did you see?
I spied seven soft seals
cast their large eyes on me:
– and I didn't find
my little fragrant one.

Did you hunt near the croft?
And what did you find?
I saw six speckled hens
pay my presence no mind:
– and I couldn't see
my little charming one.

Did you search on the shore?
And what was it you saw?
Just black-headed gulls
and a shore crab's claw:
– and I didn't find
my little dazzling one.

Did you cast about on the cliffs?
And what was it you found?
I watched a long-legged heron
glide to the ground:
– and I couldn't see
my little lovesome one.

Did you scour the fields
And what did you track down?
I came over a rabbit
with a coat reddish-brown:
– and I didn't find
my little delicate one.

Did you search in the sea?
And what had you to hand?
The floating frame of a cradle
and a fairy's grey wand:
– now I'll never chance upon
my little enchanted one.

John Rice

Roads

The road to the burn
Is pails, gossip, grey linen.

The road to the shore
Is salt and tar.

We call the track to the peats
The kestrel road.

The road to the kirk
Is a road of silences.

Ploughmen's feet
Have beaten a road to the lamp and barrel.

And the road from the shop
Is loaves, sugar, paraffin, newspapers,
    gossip.

Tinkers and shepherds
Have the whole round hill for a road.

George McKay Brown

Magic Carpet

Would you like to go to Zanzibar?
Would you like to visit Tashkent?
Eat Turkish Delight in Trebizond
Or chocolates in old Ghent?

Would you like to slip off to Cyprus
Or slide away to Greece?
Maybe zoom over the Andes,
Spend a nice weekend in Nice?

Do you like the sound of Sligo?
Do you fancy a month in Brazil?
Climb up on my Magic Carpet,
The whole thing's going to be brill!

Matt Simpson

Noisy and Quiet Places

In York
they squawk
In Leek
they shriek.
In Dore
they roar.
On Skye
they cry.
But in Llanfairgwyn-thisper-and-thistle
      they just,
        er,
         whisper and whistle.

In Stoke
they croak.
In Fleet
they bleat.
In Diss
they hiss.
In Sale
they wail.
But in Llanfairgwyn-stumble-and-stutter
      they just,
        er,
         mumble and mutter.

In Tring
they sing.
In Stone
they moan.
In Birse
they curse.
In Stroud
they're loud.
But in Llanfairgwyn-gruffle-and-griffle
    they just,
    er,
    snuffle and sniffle.

Wes Magee

A Chance in France

'Stay at home,'
Mum said,
But I,
took a chance
in France,
turned grey
for the day
in St Tropez,
forgot
what I did
in Madrid,
had some tussles
in Brussels
with a trio
from Rio,
lost my way
in Bombay,
nothing wrong
in Hong Kong,
felt calmer
in Palma,
and quite nice
in Nice,
yes, felt finer
in China,
took a room
in Khartoum

and a villa
in Manila,
had a 'do'
in Peru
with a llama
from Lima,
took a walk
in New York
with a man
from Milan,
lost a sneaker
in Costa Rica,
got lumbago
in Tobago,
felt a menace
in Venice,
was a bore
in Singapore,
lost an ear
in Korea,
some weight
in Kuwait,
tried my best
as a guest
in old Bucharest,
got the fleas
in Belize
and came home.

Pie Corbett

Mr Victor

Mr Victor's a travelling man,
    he's cycled Africa, jungle and town,
    he's warmed his feet in a Maori dawn,
    he's eaten snake from his billycan –
       he's a travelling man.

Mr Victor's a storying man,
    he's diced with death in the desert sun,
    cooked crocodile steak in his frying pan;
    he tells a tale like nobody can –
       He's a storying man.

Mr Victor's a long-living man,
    he saw the world when the world began,
    he'll stay around to the end of its span
    (or maybe longer) – at least, that's his plan,
       he's a long-living man.

Judith Nicholls

A Smuggler's Song

If you wake at midnight, and hear a horse's feet,
Don't go drawing back the blind, or looking in the street,
Them that ask no questions isn't told a lie.
Watch the wall, my darling, while the Gentlemen go by!
           Five and twenty ponies,
           Trotting through the dark –
           Brandy for the Parson,
           'Baccy for the Clerk;
           Laces for a lady, letters for a spy,
And watch the wall, my darling, while the Gentlemen go by!

Running round the woodlump if you chance to find
Little barrels, roped and tarred, all full of brandy-wine,
Don't you shout to come and look, nor use 'em for your play.
Put the brishwood back again – and they'll be gone next day!

If you see the stable-door setting open wide;
If you see a tired horse lying down inside;
If your mother mends a coat cut about and tore;
If the lining's wet and warm – don't you ask no more!

If you meet King George's men, dressed in blue and red,
You be careful what you say, and mindful what is said.
If they call you 'pretty maid,' and chuck you 'neath the chin,
Don't you tell where no one is, nor yet where no one's been!

Knocks and footsteps round the house – whistles after dark –
You've no call for running out till the house-dogs bark.
Trusty's here, and *Pincher*'s here, and see how dumb they lie –
They don't fret to follow when the Gentlemen go by!

If you do as you've been told, 'likely there's a chance,
You'll be given a dainty doll, all the way from France,
With a cap of Valenciennes, and a velvet hood –
A present from the Gentlemen, along o' being good!
      Five and twenty ponies,
      Trotting through the dark –
      Brandy for the Parson,
      'Baccy for the Clerk.
Them that asks no questions isn't told a lie –
Watch the wall, my darling, while the Gentlemen go by!

Rudyard Kipling

The Visitor

A crumbling churchyard, the sea and the moon;
The waves had gouged out grave and bone;
A man was walking, late and alone . . .

He saw a skeleton on the ground;
A ring on a bony finger he found.

He ran home to his wife and gave her the ring.
'Oh, where did you get it?' He said not a thing.

'It's the loveliest ring in the world,' she said,
As it glowed on her finger. They slipped off to bed.

At midnight they woke. In the dark outside,
'Give me my ring!' a chill voice cried.

'What was that, William? What did it say?'
'Don't worry, my dear. It'll soon go away.'

'I'm coming!' A skeleton opened the door.
'Give me my ring!' It was crossing the floor.

'What was that, William? What did it say?'
'Don't worry, my dear. It'll soon go away.'

'I'm reaching you now! I'm climbing the bed.'
The wife pulled the sheet right over her head.

It was torn from her grasp and tossed in the air:
'I'll drag you out of bed by the hair!'

'What was that, William? What did it say?'
'Throw the ring through the window! THROW IT
    AWAY!'

She threw it. The skeleton leapt from the sill,
And into the night it clattered downhill,
Fainter . . . and fainter . . . Then all was still.

Ian Serraillier

In the Time of the Wolf

Who sings the legend?
The mouse in the rafters,
the owl in the forest,
the wind in the mountains,
the tumbling river.

Where can we read it?
In a shadow on the grass,
in the footprint in the sand,
in reflections on the water,
in the fossil in the stone.

How shall we keep it
In the lake of history,
in the box called memory,
in the voice of the teller,
in the ear of the child.

How will we tell it?
With a tongue of lightning,
with a drum of thunder,
with a strumming of grasses,
with a whisper of wind.

Gillian Clarke

The Storm

See lightning is flashing,
The forest is crashing,
The rain will come dashing,
    A flood will be rising anon;

The heavens are scowling,
The thunder is growling,
The loud winds are howling,
    The storm has come suddenly on!

But now the sky clears,
The bright sun appears,
Now nobody fears,
    But soon every cloud will be gone.

Sara Coleridge

The Rain's Feet

The rain is slowly ticking over, then it picks up speed.
I can hear its tiny feet running every which way.

Why is it in such a hurry? It has the whole day
in front of it. And every new footstep is a new lead.

George Szirtes

Traditional Signs of Approaching Rain

When the green woodpecker cries
'Wet! Wet! Wet!'
When the cows play football
(circle round each other
and make a noise).
When the ducks 'do squacketty'.
When the cat scratches the table-leg,
or sneezes, or draws her paw down over
her forehead when she's washing herself.
When a cockerel flies up on to a gate, and crows.
When a dog eats grass.
When paddocks (toads) croak
on the pool at night.
When you meet a shiny-back.
When you kill a rain-clock, or God's horse.
When the hopper in the frog-spit
(or cuckoo-spit) is facing downwards.

Trad.

City Lights

Huge round oranges of light
Ripen against the thin dark of the city sky,
Spilling their juice in warm pools
        on bare dry pavements.
Below them blink the traffic lights
        like the eyes of enormous cats
Crouching in the dark –
Crouching and breathing with the
        heavy purr of the traffic;
And winking tail lights slide and dart
        like goldfish
In the pale streams pouring from
        shop windows.

Margaret Greaves

City Traffic

Green as a seedling the one lane shines,
Red ripened blooms for the opposite lines;
Emerald shoot,
Vermilion fruit.

Now amber, now champagne, now honey: go slow:
Shift, settle, than gather and sow.

Eve Merriam

City

In the morning the city
Spreads its wings
Making a song
In stone that sings.

In the evening the city
Goes to bed
Hanging lights
About its head.

Langston Hughes

Our Street

Our street is not a posh place,

Say the mums in curlers, dads in braces,
    kids in jeans
Our street is not a quiet place,

Says our football match, our honking bikes,
    our shouts.
Our street is not a tidy place,

Say the lolly wrappers, chippie bags, and
    written-on walls.
Our street is not a lazy place,

Say the car-washing dads, clothes-washing mums,
    and marbling boys.
Our street is not a short one,

Says milkman Jim, and postman Joe
    and rentman.
Our street is not a new place,

Say the paint-peeled doors, pavements worn,
  and crumbly walls.
Our street is not a green place,

Say the pavements grey, forgotten gardens,
  lines of cars.
But our street is the best

  Says me!

Les Baynton

City River

wall-slapper

factory-passer

rubbish-receiver

backstreet-winder

bridge-nudger

steps-licker

park-wanderer

summer-shiner

ducks-supporter

choppy-water

crowd-delighter

onward-traveller

June Crebbin

Country Darkness

Now is its time.
Quiet as a vixen,
happiest under the trees
in its own rustling,
country darkness is coming.

Country darkness is coming.
Stand on a wall
high above town in the cold
and watch it fall.
Now is its time.

Now is its time.
Ghostly Kingsway where nobody lives
rolls over and sleeps
in a blanket of leaves,
country darkness is coming

Country darkness is coming,
it was waiting all the time,
smelling of frost and leaves
with night up its sleeves,
now is its time.

Watch it wrapping up nightclubs
in velvety sleep,
watch it stopping
the late-night shopping,
watch it pinch out partygoers'
glittering clothes,
watch it stride into town.
Country darkness is coming –
now is its time.

Helen Dunmore

Midnight

Sleep is another country
We visit in our head.
I watch my brother sleeping now –
His eyelids heavy-smooth as lead . . .
A million miles away from me
Across our bedroom, in his bed.

It feels as if there's only me,
I'm the last boy left alive,
After the end of everything –
The last one to survive . . .
The screech owl cries, the wild wolf howls
The whole wide world's an ache.

For I am the last and lonely one
The only one left awake.

Jan Dean

Owl

Owl
Was darker
Than ebony
Flew through the night
Eyes like amber searchlights,
Rested on a post,
Feathers wind-ruffled,
Stood stump still,
Talons ready to seize
And squeeze.

Owl
Was death
That swamped the fields,
For it flew through the dark
That tightened its knot,
That bandaged the hills
In a blindfold of fear.

Owl flew – who – who – who –

Pie Corbett

Full Circle

Who . . .
      spiralled through darkness,
      a breath in the night,
      as silent as space?

Who . . .
      hovered in shadow,
      light as a halo,
      now claiming its place?

Who . . .
      searches the cornfield
      soundlessly staring
      back into space?

Judith Nicholls

Night-Spell

Close your eyes
   and wish for light
to chase away
   the net of night.

The stars are only
   down the street,
and deep in sleep
   it's there we'll meet.

Rest your head
   and dream till dawn,
in sleep be free
   as a fleet-foot fawn.

The stars are only
   down the street,
and deep in sleep
   it's there we'll meet.

Take into sleep
  this night-spell charm
to set you safe
  against all harm.

The stars are only
  down the street,
and deep in sleep
  it's there we'll meet.

John Rice

Tanka

Last night, the full moon
hung like a papery lamp
over my quiet road.
I savoured the chilly sky –
the moon tagging my shadow.

Katherine Gallagher

Moon I

bright still clean high
porthole in the morning sky

high clean still bright
space-explorer's traffic light

still bright high clean
loop-the-lunar trampoline

clean high bright still
gift on morning's window sill

Sue Cowling

Moon II

you
  spume-thrower
    wave-stretcher
      foam-snatcher
        spray-raiser
        surf-slinger
      string-puller
    scene-sifter
  tide-turner
moon

Sue Cowling

The Moon

The moon's a busy place,
full of hurrying people.
Moon birds sing on moon trees.
Purple water laps
on green spotted sand.
Far off a helicopter's landing
in a field of dancing cows.
The shops are open
all night long.

Earth's different.
It's a bowl of dust.
Wind scours the empty plains.
Visitors wear helmets.
No one stays there long.

Brian Morse

Planetarium

This is a model, which shows
the stars and planets. Look how our Earth
spins on its tilted axis; see
how it swings round the Sun in a long ellipse:
this is Night, this Day; these are the seasons.

On the long night journey home, cars
move like bubbles of light over the curved
surface of the world, heading for morning.
Too slowly for my eyes to understand,
the sky goes pale, stars fade;
hills turn their eastern faces towards the Sun.

Tony Charles

The Frozen Man

Out at the edge of town
where black trees

crack their fingers
in the icy wind

and hedges freeze
on the shadows

and breath of cattle,
still as boulders,

hangs in rags
under the rolling moon

a man is walking
alone:

on the coal-black road
his cold

feet
ring

and
ring.

Here in a snug house
at the heart of town

the fire is burning
red and yellow and gold:

you can hear the warmth
like a sleeping cat

breathe softly
in every room.

When the frozen man
comes to the door,

let him in,
let him in,
let him in.

Kit Wright

Mid-winter Haiku

Ice on the windows,
tangerines peeled in one curl
under the duvet.

Christmas in prison,
barbed wire glitters in searchlights –
a fence made of stars.

Two plastic reindeer,
a shopping bag of holly
a mouthful of frost.

Chocolate fever –
we dig for gold-wrapped treasure
deep in our stockings.

Helen Dunmore

A Boat in the Snow

On to the ocean's cold dark skin
Snowflakes are falling and are melting away.
How strange the snow seems out here!
How quickly the white blizzard is swallowed up by the
    waves.
Without the framework of land,
Each flake's transformed.
Like a trillion ocean-borne moths
They flick into existence, then go.
As the sky above and around me
Glitters with frosty flecks of stars,
So the deck of the boat glitters,
And I wonder, are whales sleeping
Out there in the world's depth, beyond
The boat's bow? And I wonder,
Do they really sleep? And how?
There is no one to ask.
Snuggled up in cabins
Passengers are dreaming,
And all round us still the snow is falling,
And the ship's deck has become
A moonlit field, a field adrift
On the dark skin of the world.
I would love to sail forever between islands of snow.

Brian Patten

November Night

Listen . . .
With faint dry sound,
Like steps of passing ghosts,
The leaves, frost-crisped, break from the trees
And fall.

Adelaide Crapsey

November

No sun – no moon!
No morn – no noon –
No dawn – no dusk – no proper time of day –
  No sky – no earthly view –
  No distance looking blue –
No road – no street no 't'other side the way' –
  No end to any Row –
  No indications where the Crescents go –
  No top to any steeple –
No recognitions of familiar people –
No courtesies for showing 'em –
  No knowing 'em –
No travelling at all – no locomotion –
No inkling of the way – no notion –
  'No go' – by land or ocean –
  No mail – no post –
No news from any foreign coast –
No Park – no Ring – no afternoon gentility –
  No company – no nobility –
No warmth, no cheerfulness, no healthful ease,
  No comfortable feel in any member –
No shade, no shine, no butterflies, no bees,
  No fruits, no flowers, no leaves, no birds –
  November!

Thomas Hood

December

De snow, de sleet, de lack of heat,
De wishy-washy sunlight,
De lip turn blue, de cold, 'ACHOO!'
De runny nose, de frostbite

De creakin' knee, de misery
De joint dem all rheumatic,
De icy bed, (de blanket dead)
De burs' pipe in de attic

De window a-shake, de glass near
  break,
De wind dat cut like razor
De wonderin' why you never buy
De window from dat double-glazer

De thick new coat, zip up to the throat,
De nose an' ears all pinky,
De weepin' sky, de clothes can't dry,
De days dem long an' inky.

De icy road, de heavy load,
De las' minute Christmas shoppin'
De cuss an' fret 'cause you feget
De ribbon an' de wrappin'.

De mud, de grime, de slush, de slime,
De place gloomy since November,
De sinkin' heart, is jus' de start, o'
De wintertime,
December.

Valerie Bloom

Christmas Fox

Driving home
down dark lanes –
only the car's beam
to light the way.

Whose amber eyes gleam,
whose ginger tail
trails into darkness?

As smart fox leaps
onto drystone walls;
becomes a shadow
that too quickly falls
into dark fields.

We pause the car,
hopeful for a glimpse.
But all that the fields yield
is a star-frosted silence.

The Christmas moon
flutters its eye

sizes up the scene –

and in the distant
  darkness
the memory of a dream
dances brush high.

Pie Corbett

Red Boots On

Way down Geneva,
All along Vine,
Deeper than the snow drift
Love's eyes shine:

Mary Lou's walking
In the winter time.

She's got

Red boots on, she's got
Red boots on,
Kicking up the winter
Till the winter's gone.

So

Go by Ontario,
Look down Main,
If you can't find Mary Lou,
Come back again:

Sweet light burning
In winter's flame.

She's got

Snow in her eyes, got
A tingle in her toes
And new red boots on
Wherever she goes

So

All around Lake Street,
Up by St Paul,
Quicker than the white wind
Love takes all:

Mary Lou's walking
In the big snow fall.

She's got

Red boots on, she's got
Red boots on,
Kicking up the winter
Till the winter's gone.

Kit Wright

Frost on the Flower

Frost on the flower,
Leaf and frond,
Snow on the field-path,
Ice on the pond.

Out of the east
A white wind comes.
Hail on the rooftop
Kettledrums.

Snow-fog wanders
Hollow and hill.
Along the valley
The stream is still.

Thunder and lightning.
Down slaps the ram.
No doubt about it.
Summer again.

Charles Causley

Ten Syllables for Spring

daffylonglegs
blowing
buttered trumpets

Sue Cowling

Slowly

Slowly the tide creeps up the sand,
Slowly the shadows cross the land.
Slowly the carthorse pulls his mile,
Slowly the old man mounts the stile.

Slowly the hands move round the clock,
Slowly the dew dries on the dock.
Slow is the snail – but slowest of all
the green moss spreads on the old brick wall.

James Reeves

Poem on Bread

The poet is about to write a poem;
He does not use a pencil or a pen.
He dips his long thin finger into jam
Or something savoury preferred by men.
This poet does not choose to write on paper;
He takes a single slice of well-baked bread
And with his jam or marmite-nibbed forefinger
He writes his verses down on that instead.
His poem is fairly short as all the best are.
When he has finished it he hopes that you
Or someone else – your brother, friend or sister –
Will read and find it marvellous and true.
If you can't read, then eat: it tastes quite good.
If you do neither, all that I can say
Is he who needs no poetry or bread
Is really in a devilish bad way.

Vernon Scannell

Where Do Ideas Come From?

I once found an idea for a poem
Down the back of the sofa.
It was just out of reach,
Which was annoying,
And I had to reach down
Behind the cushions,
Right up to my elbow,
To fetch it out.

I also found a pound coin.

Roger Stevens

Unfolding Bud

One is amazed
By a water-lily bud
Unfolding
With each passing day,
Taking on a richer colour
And new dimensions.

One is not amazed,
At a first glance,
By a poem,
Which is as tight-closed
As a tiny bud.

Yet one is surprised
To see the poem
Gradually unfolding,
Revealing its rich inner self,
As one reads it
Again
And over again.

Naoshi Koriyama (Japan)

Answer to *How Did He Escape?*

He rubbed his hands
till they were sore.

He took the saw
and cut the table
right in half.

Two halves make a whole.

So he climbed through the hole.

Once outside –
he cried
till he was hoarse.

He climbed on the horse
and rode away . . .

Pie Corbett

Acknowledgements

The compiler and publishers wish to thank the following for permission to use copyright material:

John Agard, 'Rat Race', Hippo Writes a Love Poem to His Wife' and 'Hippo Writes a Love Poem to Her Husband' from *We Animals Would Like a Word With You* by John Agard, Red Fox (1996), by permission of Caroline Sheldon Literary Agency on behalf of the author; **Les Baynton**, 'Our Street', by permission of the author; **James Berry**, 'Playing a Dazzler' from *Playing a Dazzler* by James Berry, Hamish Hamilton, by permission of PFD on behalf of the author; **Clare Bevan**, 'Playground Song', by permission of the author; **Valerie Bloom**, 'De' from *Let Me Touch the Sky*, Macmillan (2000), by permission of the author; **Ann Bonner**, 'Gorilla', by permission of the author; **George Mackay Brown**, 'Roads' from *Selected Poems 1954-1991* by George Mackay Brown, by permission of John Murray (Publishers) Ltd; **Dave Calder**, 'Where?', by permission of the author; **Charles Causley**, 'Frost on the Flower' from *Collected Poems* by Charles Causley, Macmillan, by permission of David Higham Associates on behalf of the author; **Deborah Chandra**, 'Porch Light' from *Rich Lizard and Other Poems* by Deborah Chandra. Copyright © 1993 by Deborah Chandra, by permission of Farrar, Straus and Giroux, LLC; **Tony Charles**, 'Planetarium', 'Rabbit and Dragon' and 'Hippopotamus', by permission of the author; **Gillian Clarke**, 'In the Time of the Wolf' from *The Animal Wall* by Gillian Clarke, Pont Books, Gomer Press (1990), by permission of the author; **Sue Cowling**, 'Ten Syllables for Spring', 'Moon I', 'Moon II', 'Funny How She Forgets' and 'Waiting', by permission of the author; **June Crebbin**, 'City River' from *Cows Moo, Cars Toot* by June Crebbin, by permission of Penguin Books Ltd; **Jan Dean**, 'Midnight', by permission of the author; **Bernard Dadie**, 'Dry Your Tears Africa', by permission of Editions Robert Laffont; **Gina Douthwaite**, 'Snout Doing', by permission of the author; **Helen Dunmore**, 'Mid-Winter Haiku' and 'Country Darkness' from *Secrets* by Helen Dunmore, by permission of A P Watt Ltd on behalf of the author; **Chris Eddershaw**, 'May Bugs', by permission of the author; **Katherine Gallagher**, 'Tanka', by permission of the author; **Jean Gill**, 'Trying It On', included in *The Poet's House*, ed. Jude Brigley, Pont Books, Gomer Press (2000), by permission of the author; **Margaret Greaves**, 'City Lights', by permission of Marilyn Malin on behalf of the author; **Michael Harrison**, 'Miss! Sue is Kissing' included in *Junk Mail*, Oxford University Press (1993), by permission of the author; **Langston Hughes**, 'City' from *Collected Poems* by Langston Hughes, by permission of David Higham Associates on behalf of the author; **Robert Hull**, 'Self Advert for Mole Programme Tonight' from *Stargrazer* by Robert Hull, Hodder Children's Books (1997), by permission of PFD on behalf of the author; **Rudyard Kipling**, 'A Smuggler's Song', by permission of A P Watt on behalf of The National Trust for Places of Historical Interest or Natural Beauty; **Naoshi Koriyama**, 'Unfolding Bud', first appeared in *The Christian Science Monitor*, 3.7.57. Copyright © 1957 The Christian Science Monitor, by permission of The Christian Science Monitor; **Wes Magee**, 'Noisy and Quiet Places' from *The Boneyard Rap* by Wes Magee, Hodder/Wayland (2000), by permission of the author; **Eve Merriam**, 'City Traffic' from *It Doesn't Have to Rhyme* by Eve Merriam. Copyright © 1964, 1992 by Eve Merriam, by permission of Marian Reiner on behalf of the author; **John Mole**, 'Sometimes' from *The Doctor's Dilemma* by John Mole, Hodder & Stoughton (1999), and 'Taking the Plunge' from *Boo to a Goose* by John Mole, Peterloo Poets (1987), by permission of the author; **Michaela Morgan**, 'Blake's Tiger – Revisited', first published in *Through the Window*, compiled by Wendy Body, by permission of the author; and 'The Day the Zoo Escaped' from *Big Book Phonics* by Michaela Morgan and Sue Palmer, by permission from the authors; **Brian Morse**, 'Cat in the Window' from *Picnic On The Moon* by Brian Morse, Macmillan (1993), 'The Moon' and 'My Cat Syllable', by permission of the author; **Brian Moses**, 'Stick Insect' from *I Wish I Could Dine With a Porcupine* by Brian Moses, Hodder/Wayland (2000), by permission of the author; **Judith Nicholls**, 'Mr Victor' from *Dragonsfire* by Judith Nicholls, Faber and Faber. Copyright © 1990 Judith Nicholls, 'The Dare', 'DIY UFO Poem' and 'Full Circle'. Copyright © Judith Nicholls 2002, by permission of the author; **Brian Patten**, 'A Boat in the Snow' from *Juggling With Jerbils* by Brian Patten, Puffin Books (2000). Copyright © Brian Patten 2000, by permission of Rogers, Coleridge & White on behalf of the author; **James Reeves**, 'Jargon' and 'Slowly' from *Complete Poems for Children* by James Reeves, Heinemann, by permission of Laura Cecil Literary Agency on behalf of the Estate of the author; **John Rice**, 'Night Spell and 'Cradle Song' from *The Dream of Night Fishers*, Scottish Cultural Press (1998), by permission of the author; **Carl Sandburg**, 'We Must Be Polite' from *The Complete Poems of Carl Sandburg*. Copyright © 1970, 1969 by Lilian Steichen Sandburg, Trustee, by permission of Harcourt, Inc; **Vernon Scannell**, 'Poem on Bread', by permission of the author; **Ian Serraillier**, 'The Visitor', by permission of Anne Serraillier; **Matt Simpson**, 'Magic Carpet', by permission of the author; **Roger Stevens**, 'Where Do Ideas Come From?' from *I Did Not Eat the Goldfish* by Roger Stevens, Macmillan Children's Books (2002), by permission of the author; **Judith Viorst**, 'And After A Hundred Years . . .', 'And Beauty and The Beast . . .' and 'While Poor Hansel Was Locked . . .' from *Sad Underwear* by Judith Viorst, Alladin Paperbacks (2000). Copyright © Judith Viorst 2000, by permission of A M Heath & Co Ltd on behalf of the author; **Kit Wright,** 'Red Boots On' from *Hoping It Might Be So* by Kit Wright, Leviathan (2000), and 'The Frozen Man' from *Rabbiting On* by Kit Wright, Collins (1978), by permission of the author.

Every effort has been made to trace the copyright holders but if any have been inadvertently overlooked the publishers will be pleased to make the necessary arrangement at the first opportunity.